LEARNING TO READ
WHILE READING TO LEARN
SERIES

The Big

Story by Joan B. Ominsky
Art by Stanton Keeney

Break

Jo Stanchfield
S. I. Hayakawa
Ralph Kellogg
Frank Hutchinson

PRODUCED BY CENTURY COMMUNICATIONS · SAN FRANCISCO
FOR CENTURY CONSULTANTS, A DIVISION OF COMBINED REGISTRY
COMPANY, CHICAGO, ILLINOIS

Contents

Main Characters

Dennis

Harold

Mike

Derek

How to Use Your
"Key to Better Reading"

guitar as in gun; guitar as in star
is the way to say guitar

Gun and *star* (words you already know) are clue words for the pronunciation of the word *guitar*.

The gui in *guitar* and the gu in *gun* are printed in color. This means that these parts of the two words sound the same.

The ar in the words *guitar* and *star* are printed in color, too. This means that these parts of the two words sound the same.

Sounding out the parts in the clue words that are printed in color will help you to read, or decode, the word *guitar*.

A "Key to Better Reading" may be found on most pages of this book. The clue words in this key will help you in reading, or decoding, the "unknown" words on the page. You may also discover that the "unknown" word is not unknown at all, but one that you often hear and use when you talk. It is just that you did not recognize it when you saw it in print.

About the Book

This is the story of four boys whose excitement over rock 'n' roll music brings them together to form a group, the Southside Strummers.

The four boys—Harold, Dennis, Derek, and Mike— discover that they have much to learn when they set out to make a name for themselves. They work hard and have fun, but they run into some rough problems along the way.

Harold, whom the other boys have chosen as their leader, sets up the Southside Strummers' first engagement—playing for a dance at the Youth Center. As time goes on, the boys get more and more engagements and become more and more successful.

When the Strummers play in public, the crowd goes wild. Girls scream. Boys stomp and whistle. The Strummers' publicity skyrockets.

In spite of their success, the four musicians have a serious problem. The way in which they solve this problem makes exciting reading, especially for someone who likes rock 'n' roll music.

Chapter 1

Looking Ahead

Harold, leader of the Southside Strummers, has a surprise for the other members. He has gotten a date for them to play at a dance. Harold has doubts, however, about the other boys, and wonders if they can succeed. They often would rather clown around than work to improve their musical talents.

Mike believes the group needs a manager to find playing engagements for them, but they haven't found anyone willing to take the job.

Harold has to take his sister Donna and her friend Janet on an errand that later proves to be of help to the boys.

You may find some words that are new to you. If these words give you trouble, look at the pronunciation guides. In addition, you may want to look up some of these words in a dictionary.

Some words in this chapter that you may want to check are *skeptical*, *reputation*, *rhythmic*, *scholarship*, *vocalist*, *instrument*, and *fabric*.

Great Chance

Harold jumped off the bus and started running toward his home. He could hardly wait to get there with the good news. He and the other guys in the band were going to play at the Youth Center Friday night.

The guys would be really surprised. Their first public appearance!

Harold thought about the group as he ran along. It had been tough getting started. Mr. Brown, the music teacher at Greenwich High School, thought that the four of them were good enough to make it as a rock 'n' roll band. At first, Harold had been skeptical. He didn't know whether or not he could depend on the others.

> skeptical as in sketch; skeptical as in kept;
> skeptical as in comical

Mike had the reputation at school of being a goof-off. Dennis and Derek were brothers and great guys, but they were kind of lazy, and Derek was a clown. Anyhow, they went ahead with the idea, the four of them, and started the Southside Strummers.

Most of their practicing was done in Harold's folks' garage. The others lived in apartments, and the noise from the band would drive people wild. Even Harold's mother complained sometimes, but she really didn't mind.

Harold stopped in front of his garage and pulled up the door.

"Hey, guys, listen to the news. I've got us a job," he shouted.

> reputation as in crept; reputation as in young;
> reputation as in nation

The rhythmic beat of the drums drowned out Harold's voice.

Harold walked over to Mike and grabbed his arms from behind. "Stop the noise, kid, and listen to the good news. I've got us a job," Harold shouted again.

Mike and Dennis stopped playing, while Derek continued to strum his guitar softly. "A job, a job, Harold has got us a job," Derek sang.

Then he stopped, too.

"Give, man," the three shouted excitedly. "Where? When? How much?"

---

rhythmic as in rib; rhythmic as in with; rhythmic as in stick

guitar as in gun; guitar as in star

"Take it easy," said Harold. "The where is the Youth Center. The when is Friday night. The how much is nothing."

"What do you mean nothing?" asked Mike.

"Nothing," Harold repeated. "Listen you guys, this is a great chance. Stop being so greedy. First we have to prove that we can play before someone is going to pay to listen to us."

"Harold's right," said Mike. "Besides he's the boss. We agreed on that, so let him handle it."

"Okay, okay," the other two agreed. Then Derek added, "I guess Harold's right. We've been trying to get a paying spot for over two months. Everyone wants to know where we've played before. When they hear we haven't, the answer is always the same, 'Sorry, we need someone with experience.' "

Dennis looked at his brother. "Right," he said. "Anyway, we always practice on Friday night. This time we'll just do it in front of an audience."

This issue settled, the boys started playing again.

* * *

Later, Mike said, "We really need a manager. It doesn't seem fair to have Harold chase all over town trying to find us jobs."

experience as in it; experience as in story;
  experience as in silence
audience as in August; audience as in silence
issue as in wish; issue as in blue

12

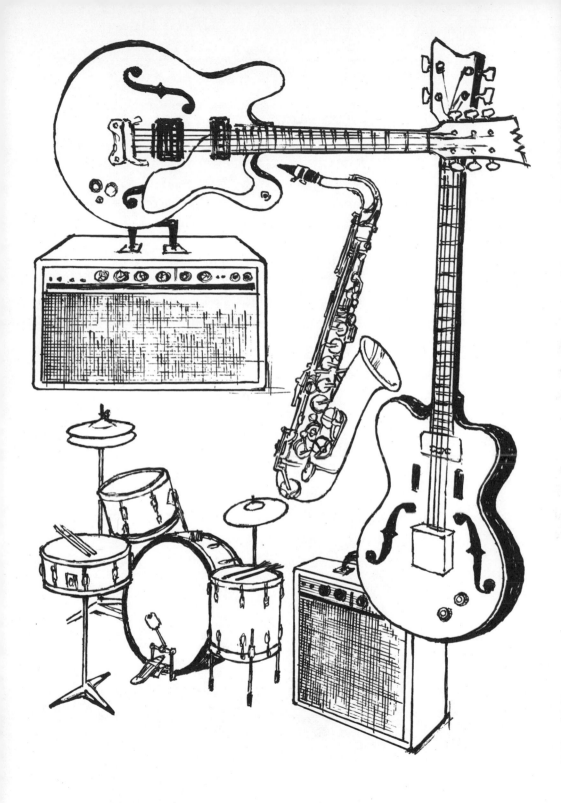

scholarship as in scoff; scholarship as in dollar;
   scholarship as in ship
material as in upon; material as in ear
costumes as in cot; costumes as in tube

Harold said, "You know how hard it is to get a manager, especially when you're unknown."

"I'll be your manager," a girl's voice said from the door.

"Not you again," Harold said to his sister Donna. Then he turned and smiled at Donna's friend. "Hi, Janet, how's the singing coming?"

"Fine," Janet said. "Mr. Brown said he might get me a scholarship next year."

"Great," shouted Derek and Dennis.

"Harold, Mom said you could take Janet and me to pick up the material for our costumes," Donna said.

"Do you think that's all I have to do? We're playing at the Youth Center on Friday, Donna," Harold told his sister and Janet.

"Gee," Janet said. "That's something. I don't suppose you need a girl vocalist?" She gave the boys a pleading look.

"You're out of it, girl," Mike said. "We all agreed when we formed the group—no girls."

"They hate girls," Donna said to her friend. Then she turned to Harold. "You'd better drive us down to pick up our material. We need to start making our costumes for the play. They have to be ready for dress rehearsal. That's only three weeks away."

---

vocalist as in vote; vocalist as in ankle;
   vocalist as in list
rehearsal as in rich; rehearsal as in her;
   rehearsal as in final

"Wait in the car," Harold ordered. "You guys go on with the jam session if you want." He put on his jacket and fished around in his pocket for the car keys. The others started playing again as Harold went out the door.

Harold started the motor of his old hardtop. Donna and Janet were squeezed into the front seat beside him. Instrument cases and music stands filled the back seat.

The sound of a pleasant baritone voice drifted through the open car window as Harold backed down

> instrument as in skin; instrument as in struck;
>   instrument as in moment
> baritone as in carry; baritone as in stone

the driveway away from the garage. "Hey, who's singing? He's terrific," Janet said.

"That's Derek," Harold told her. "He's great. He also plays a mean guitar. Everybody in the group has to play and sing."

"No use trying to persuade him to let you join the group, Janet," Donna told her friend. "They won't listen to anything you say."

The two girls remained silent the rest of the way.

Harold squeezed into a parking place and told the girls to hurry up. They ran into the fabric shop and were back in the car within a few minutes.

"Gee, this is really neat," Janet said fingering the striped material, sticking out of the bag.

"Look at it, Harold. Don't you think it will make dreamy costumes?" Donna asked.

Harold glanced down at the cloth. "I guess so," he mumbled. "But it looks like it was meant more for men's shirts than for girls' dresses."

Janet and Donna broke into laughter. "It's supposed to." Janet giggled. "Donna and I are playing the role of two brothers in the play."

"Oh, no," Harold groaned. "Now I've heard everything. Don't they have any boys in that drama class?"

"Of course, they do. This is a musical, and these two parts are always sung by girls. That's the way the man wrote it."

Looking Back

Now that you have read the first chapter of the book, think about what you have read. This will help you understand why things happen the way they do as the story progresses.

Do you think Harold had good reasons for doubting his friends?

The boys were disappointed that they were not paid for playing at the Youth Center. Do you believe money is the only reward a person should expect for his work? What reward did Harold, Mike, Dennis, and Derek believe they would get since they were not going to be rewarded with money?

Are there rewards more valuable than material things?

Chapter 2

Looking Ahead

It is time for the Friday night dance. The boys have done some extra work to make the dance and their group successful. The young dancers are excited by the group's music and enthusiastically show their approval.

Harold and his group accept another playing date. This time they will be paid! Still, they need costumes for the next dance.

See if you would solve this problem as they do. They take the easiest way offered them. Do you believe taking the easiest way is always the best way?

Use the pronunciation guides found on most pages of this book to help you with new words. Then check your dictionary to be sure you understand the meanings of the words as they are used in the story. Then see how many other meanings the words may have.

This practice will help you improve your reading, speaking, and writing. Some words to watch for are *enthusiastically, intermission, approached*, and *improvised*.

Date for Pay

Friday night finally arrived. The boys had been busy the past few days. Dennis and Derek had cut some large wooden letters spelling out the group's name. They were painted gold. Harold watched as the two boys fastened them above the bandstand.

Mike walked over to Harold and said, "It looks like it'll be a big crowd. I'm sure glad we got those posters out."

"The posters got the people here. I just hope they like us and tell their friends," Harold replied. "Then maybe we'll get some real paying dates. Say, we'd better get started. It's almost eight o'clock."

bandstand as in and; band + stand = bandstand

Harold and Mike hurriedly joined Derek and Dennis on the bandstand. Harold helped the other boys tune their instruments. When they were ready, he walked up to the mike and introduced the group.

Janet and Donna were sitting near the bandstand. When Harold began to speak, they both started screaming enthusiastically. The rest of the girls joined in. The boys whistled.

When they had finally quieted down, the Strummers started playing. The Youth Center jumped. Teenagers filled the floor. They moved eagerly to the music of the Southside Strummers. Mike pounded wildly on his drums. Dennis and Derek stood in front of the group, strumming away on their guitars. Harold stood to the side with his saxophone. His bass guitar stood against the wall. He would play it later.

At first the boys sang together. Then Derek took over as soloist. His clear deep voice filled the auditorium. Girls again screamed their approval. Soon almost everyone stopped dancing. Boys and girls

enthusiastically as in hen; enthusiastically as in choose;
  enthusiastically as in crazy;
  enthusiastically as in plastic;
  enthusiastically as in comically
saxophone as in sack; saxophone as in sun;
  saxophone as in fold; saxophone as in telephone
soloist as in toe; soloist as in wrist
auditorium as in August; auditorium as in story

23

stood around the band, clapping their hands and shouting for more. The crowd sure seems to love us, Harold thought.

During intermission admirers swarmed around the band. "Great sound, great," said one boy.

"You're just what this neighborhood needs," another boy added, "a groovy new sound."

Girls crowded around Derek. "Sing, Derek, sing," a girl with long hair shouted.

"Seems like we went over big," Harold said happily to the others when they got ready to play again.

intermission as in winter; intermission as in wish;
   intermission as in until
admirers as in had; admirers as in fire;
   admirers as in hers
groovy as in grew; groovy as in movie

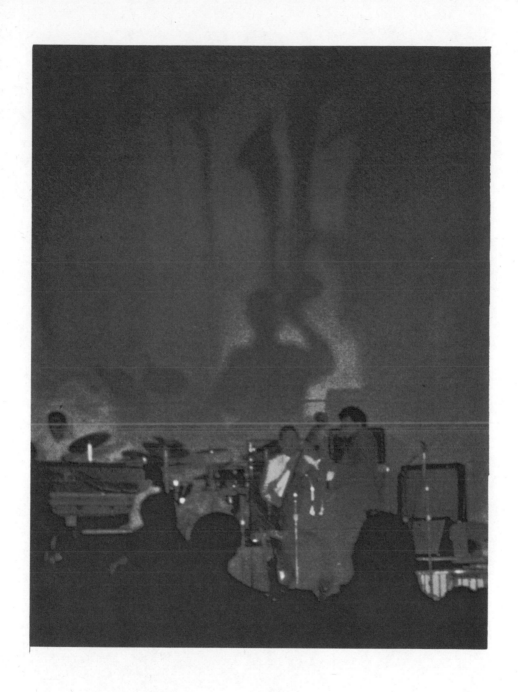

"Looks that way," Mike agreed, giving his drums a roll.

As the boys ended their last song, a young man in his twenties approached Harold.

"Got a great band there," he said.

"Thank you," Harold answered, his face beaming. "Glad you like us."

"Bob Martin's the name," the young man said, extending his hand. "I'm from the YMCA. I want to make you fellows an offer. How would you like to play over at the 'Y' next Friday?"

"Wow, we'd love it!" Harold exclaimed. "Wouldn't we, fellows?"

"Sure would," the other boys agreed.

approached as in upon; approached as in coached

"We don't have much money," Bob said. "What we usually do is give the band fifty per cent of the gate."

Mike looked embarrassed when he asked, "What do you mean by fifty per cent of the gate?"

"Oh, that's simple," Harold told him. "We get half of the money that comes in. If the 'Y' takes in fifty dollars, we get twenty-five dollars. If it takes in a hundred dollars, we get fifty dollars."

"Sounds all right," Derek said.

"Good, then it's a deal," Bob Martin said.

Harold asked, "What time do you want us there?"

"About eight o'clock should do it," Bob answered. "See you." He waved good-bye to the boys.

Mike started pounding his drums. "Who'd have thought we'd come up with a real paying job so soon?" he asked.

"It's great. Just great," Derek said excitedly. He pranced around the empty stage and improvised a tune,

> "We're on our way, on our way,
> Got a playing date for pay,
> Got a date for pay."

"Sing it, Derek! Sing it!" Harold laughed. "We really have something to sing about."

---

embarrassed as in them; embarrassed as in carry;
   embarrassed as in rust
improvised as in him; improvised as in rug;
   improvised as in prized

The boys clowned around as they packed up their instruments and music. Then Harold saw Donna and Janet walk up to them.

"I almost forgot, I promised Mom to see that the girls got home," Harold said. "I'd better get going."

Harold said to Donna and Janet, "Could you girls carry the music out to the car? Then we'll be on our way."

"Hold on a minute. We've got a few things to decide if we're going to play for pay next Friday. What kind of costumes can we come up with by then?" Mike asked.

The girls started asking questions, and Derek quickly brought them up to date.

"It's just great, except for one thing," Derek said. "We need some fancy costumes or at least some flashy shirts to wear for our first date."

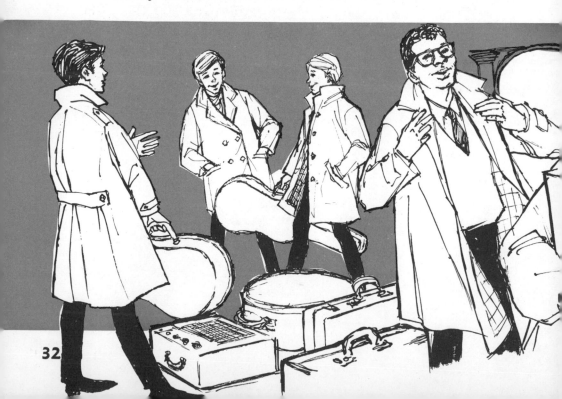

Donna and Janet looked at each other. Then Janet spoke up. "We could lend you our material for shirts. We could even make them for you, so they wouldn't cost so much. But you'd have to promise to pay us by next Saturday so we can buy more material for our own costumes."

"Good," Mike said to the girls, "that sounds like just what we need."

"Wait a minute," Dennis said. "What if we don't make a lot of money next Friday?"

"Oh, we'll make enough to pay the girls back. You saw the crowd here tonight. Man, they loved us. Bet you every one of them turns up at the 'Y' next Friday," Derek said.

"I don't know," Dennis said. But the others over-ruled him.

The Strummers broke up. Harold drove the girls home. Now we're really on our way, he thought.

Looking Back

Now that you know the boys better, what do you think of their success at the dance? Do you believe that the posters they made to advertise the dance were responsible for their popularity? Or, was it because they had worked hard rehearsing their music and so were able to do a fine job singing and playing?

Do you think Dennis showed good judgment in not wanting to borrow for the group's new shirts? Why?

Perhaps you have a favorite musical group. It could be interesting to find out how the group got started. You may want to write a composition comparing it and the Southside Strummers.

Do you think being able to play the guitar and sing is enough to start a musical group in business? What other things might be considered?

Chapter 3

Looking Ahead

The girls finish the new shirts for the Strummers just in time for them to keep their playing date at the "Y." The boys are eager and excited, but something they had not expected has happened.

There is always a chance that things will not come out as a person plans. The weather, a chance meeting, and many other things can keep plans from turning out as expected.

The Strummers are happy about one unexpected event. They get a manager. You will want to find out what kind of man he is.

Harold has a strong feeling that he should be cautious about something, but he does not take his own advice.

Have you ever done things you felt you shouldn't because you wanted to be popular with your group? If you have, you will understand why Harold acts as he does.

Remember, it is good practice to look up in a dictionary any words that you do not understand in your reading. Some words that you may want to look up are *reception*, *ultimate*, *gratitude*, *contract*, *hesitantly*, and *percentage*.

Money Trouble

Donna and Janet were still putting the finishing touches on the boys' shirts the following Friday night —only an hour before the dance.

"Hurry up, will ya," Harold told Donna. "We can't be late for our first big paying date."

"Take it easy," Derek interrupted. "The girls can only work so fast."

"Yeah," Mike agreed, admiring his new shirt in the mirror.

Donna sewed on the last button, and Harold put on his shirt. Dennis had already begun gathering up the music and taking instruments out to the car.

> interrupted as in skin; interrupted as in tub;
> interrupted as in erupt

"Guess we're ready. Everybody climb in," Harold said as he walked from the garage to the car in the driveway.

The girls were sandwiched between Dennis and the instruments in the back seat of the old car. "Hey, take it easy," Dennis said when Harold rounded a curve. "These instruments and music stands poke us enough back here without you helping them along."

Harold slowed down.

Soon they arrived at the "Y."

Driving rain caused them to bend their heads down and shield their instruments against the storm. They rushed into the building.

"Whew, it's good to be inside," Derek said as he wiped his guitar dry.

Janet and Donna hurriedly set up the music stands and sorted out the music. The boys began tuning their instruments.

"Get a move on," Harold said as Mike began clowning around with his drums. "We've only got ten minutes until we start playing."

"Okay, okay." Mike grinned. Then his face became serious. "There aren't too many people here yet," he said, looking at a handful of teenagers shaking their raincoats and umbrellas at the far end of the room.

"More will show up soon, you'll see," Janet said cheerfully.

The boys began playing.

When the boys broke for intermission, Harold said, "This place is still half empty."

The crowd that did show up seemed to enjoy the music, but the Southside Strummers didn't get the big reception they'd had at the Youth Center.

"Guess the weather is casting a gloom on the audience, too," Dennis said. "At this rate, we won't make enough to pay the girls for their material."

The boys went back to their music. They played well. But each worried how they would be able to pay back Donna and Janet. They didn't want to spoil the girls' play.

The dance ended. The boys began packing up their instruments.

Bob Martin walked over to the group. "Here you are, fellows," he said, handing them a check. "Did a great job. Everyone loved you."

Bob noticed their gloomy faces and added, "Sorry about the crowd tonight. But you know how it is. We have no money for advertising. With the rain and all, only a small crowd turned up."

Harold looked at the check. "Well guys," he said, passing it around, "that's it—seven-fifty. We'll have to think of another way to earn some more money to pay the girls. Anyone have any suggestions?"

The boys stared gloomily at each other.

---

reception as in rich; reception as in September;
reception as in nation

Then Harold saw a man approaching them. Harold had noticed him before, standing quietly by himself, listening. He wore a dark sport coat, tight pants, and a yellow shirt. He seemed to be in his early thirties. Sunglasses shaded his eyes. Speaking in a slow, casual style he said, "Got a good band there, fellows."

"Oh, thanks—thanks a lot," Harold said. "Right now we've got our problems."

"Maybe I can help," said the man. He put out his hand for Harold to shake. "Jim Sharp's the name. Pleased to meet you. What's yours?"

"I'm Harold Williams," Harold said. Then he introduced the other band members.

"Pleased to meet you all," Jim said in his slow drawl. "Maybe we can do business together, boys. Did you fellows ever think of getting a manager?"

"Yeah, we've thought of it," Harold answered, "but we don't know any."

"Well," Jim said, "I thought maybe I'd take care of you. I've done this kind of thing before. You've heard of the rock group called the 'Ultimates'? I

---

introduced as in skin; introduced as in trust;
   introduced as in produced
ultimates as in dull; ultimates as in tub;
   ultimates as in admits

gratitude as in rat; gratitude as in tube
possibilities as in hospital; possibilities as in upon;
   possibilities as in bill; possibilities as in duties
guarantee as in carry; guarantee as in run

was their manager. Gave them their start. When
they started hitting the big time I got dropped. That's
gratitude for you. Now I'm looking for a new young
group to build up. I think that you guys have real
possibilities."

"Gee," Derek said, "you really managed the
Ultimates? Boy, they're big stars now."

"That's right," Jim answered, "and I can do the
same for you. You're a sharp group. You just need
some experience. Need to play in the right places. I
know this business cold. I'm the guy who can put
you on top. In six months, I guarantee, you'll be so

famous, you'll have your own fan clubs and be regulars on television. In a year you'll even be cutting records. Everything that goes along with being stars."

Harold wondered why this man would bother with them if he was such a big shot. I guess he's just interested in new groups, Harold thought.

"Sounds great to me!" shouted Mike. "What do you guys think?"

"We've got nothing to lose, do we?" Dennis looked at the other band members.

"You're right," Derek agreed. "We need a man with experience to get us bookings. I'm game."

"Me, too," Mike agreed. "As I said before, it's not fair to have Harold do all the running around for us."

"Good," Jim said, putting a piece of gum into his mouth. "And to show you I'm an all-right guy I'll advance you twenty-five bucks. You've probably had plenty of expenses! This will help you out until you hit the big time."

advance as in had; advance as in dance

> contract as in cot; contract as in trap;
>   contract as in fact
> hesitantly as in says; hesitantly as in stunt;
>   hesitantly as in only

"Great," Harold said. "We have to pay back my sister for some material. Thanks, Jim, thanks a million."

Jim handed Harold the twenty-five dollars and asked, "Now how about making everything official and signing a contract?"

"What's that?" Mike asked.

"Oh, you know," Jim replied, "that's a legal paper that puts our agreement on the up-and-up. You'll get to know about all these things when you're really in show biz. A contract says just what your manager is expected to do for you."

Jim pulled out a long printed paper and showed it to the boys.

Harold went over and looked at it quickly. The print was small. It would take half an hour to read it! "There're a lot of words there," he said, hesitantly.

percentage as in person; percentage as in sent; percentage as in bridge

"Don't worry about it," Jim said. "It says in a lot of fancy legal language that I'm supposed to get you jobs. For each job, I get paid a percentage of your take. Sound fair?"

"How big a percentage do you get?" Harold asked.

"Oh, the usual," Jim replied. "I get ten per cent, plus expenses. It's all in the contract. Here, take a look."

Harold looked again at the contract. Maybe he should take it home and read it. But he knew the guys would tease him for being so cautious. And if Jim thought Harold didn't trust him, he might get mad and tell them to forget the whole thing.

He knew the other boys were waiting for his decision. Suddenly he brushed the contract aside and held out his hand for Jim to shake.

"Okay, Jim. You get ten per cent plus expenses. I think we can all agree on that. Right, guys?"

The other boys nodded their approval.

"Then all that's left is for each of you to sign on the dotted line," Jim said, pulling out a gold pen from his pocket. One by one, the boys signed their names to the contract.

"Guess that settles that," Jim said. He put the signed contract into his pocket. "Got to run now."

The boys couldn't believe their luck—money to repay Donna and Janet and a manager to boot. They sang and laughed all the way home. Only Harold was a little quieter than usual. He was thinking of the decision he had made. He hoped it was the right one.

decision as in did; decision as in silk;
decision as in division

Looking Back

The boys were disappointed because they could not pay Donna and Janet for making their new shirts. Do you think the boys showed the proper appreciation to the girls for helping them out?

The unexpected rain kept people away from the dance. How did the boys manage to pay back Janet and Donna?

The Strummers now have a manager. What kind of man do you think Jim Sharp is? What is a contract?

Do you think Harold would have been wiser had he taken the contract home to read before he and the boys signed it? Should he have shown the contract to someone older?

Chapter 4

Looking Ahead

Mr. Brown, the school band teacher, again helps the Southside Strummers on their way. He tells Harold that the newspaper is sponsoring a contest. It could give them the chance they need to perform before a large audience.

There is a disappointment that the boys have to overcome, but it is followed by an exciting surprise.

Jim Sharp comes to see the boys again, and Harold can't help feeling that something is wrong. Do you trust Jim? Do you think the boys should find out more about the duties and responsibilities that a manager has toward his clients?

Watch for new words in your reading. Use the pronunciation guides found on most pages of this book to help you with your reading. Check your dictionary to be sure you understand the meanings of the words as they are used in the story. Then see how many other meanings the words may have.

Some words you may want to look up are *festival, critics, optimistically,* and *spectacular.*

T. V. Date

A week after the boys had hired Jim Sharp as their manager, Mr. Brown stopped Harold as he was leaving band class.

"I heard about the big hit your band made at the Youth Center," said Mr. Brown. "Been having any luck since?"

"Well, we played at the 'Y' the next week, but there weren't too many people there. It was raining that night."

"That's too bad. Well, it takes a while to get started in this business, you know," said the teacher.

"Oh, I think our luck is going to change now, Mr. Brown. We got ourselves a manager. He's going to do our publicity and arrange for cool new costumes

publicity as in public; publicity as in listen;
publicity as in duty

festival as in fester; festival as in upon

sponsoring as in pond; sponsoring as in sir

and. . ." Harold stopped. He couldn't think of anything else a manager was supposed to do.

"Great," said Mr. Brown. "Who is he? Friend of
yours?"

"Oh, no. We were lucky. He happened to hear us
play at the 'Y' the other night. He came up and
offered to manage the group."

"Well, fine," said Mr. Brown. "I'd like to meet him
someday."

Mr. Brown continued. "By the way, there's
going to be a rock 'n' roll festival at Golden Gate
Park next Saturday afternoon. The newspaper is
sponsoring it. They want to give some new groups a

critics as in crib; critics as in sticks

miniature as in pony; miniature as in upon;
    miniature as in picture

fantastically as in man; fantastically as in plastic;
    fantastically as in comically

microphone as in my; microphone as in crust;
    microphone as in fold;
    microphone as in telephone

chance to be heard. You'll have to compete with other groups. Some of them are outstanding. The festival is supposed to draw a huge crowd. Lots of people could hear you. The paper is going to have some rock 'n' roll critics there. They'll choose the best group and award them a miniature silver guitar. Best of all," he finished, "the winning group gets a TV appearance on Art Wilson's show."

"Wow!" Harold shouted. "That sounds great. What a break winning would be! I can't wait to tell the guys. We'll be there for sure." He thanked Mr. Brown and raced down the hall to his next class.

At the rock 'n' roll festival, the boys listened to the other groups. Some were fantastically good, Harold thought.

When their turn came, they played like they had never played before. The crowd—mostly teenagers—screamed and whistled. Harold thought they screamed and whistled louder for the Southside Strummers than for any of the other groups.

After all groups had had their chance, the judges huddled together and talked. Then one of the judges walked over to the microphone.

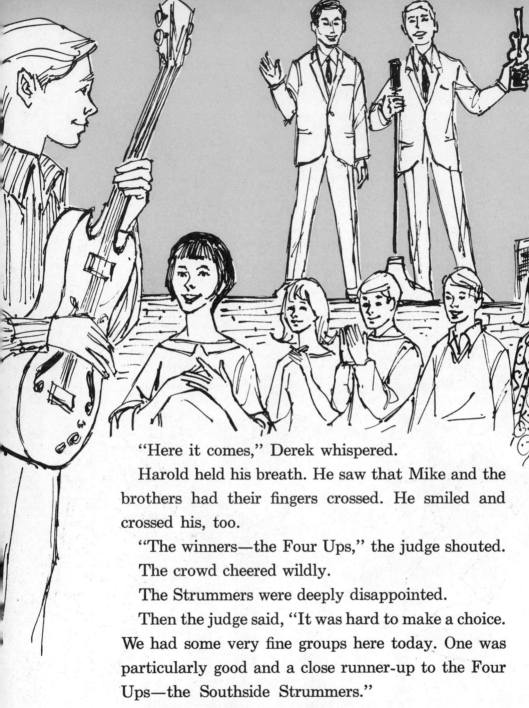

"Here it comes," Derek whispered.

Harold held his breath. He saw that Mike and the brothers had their fingers crossed. He smiled and crossed his, too.

"The winners—the Four Ups," the judge shouted.

The crowd cheered wildly.

The Strummers were deeply disappointed.

Then the judge said, "It was hard to make a choice. We had some very fine groups here today. One was particularly good and a close runner-up to the Four Ups—the Southside Strummers."

The crowd cheered again.

"Did you hear that, guys," shouted Mike. "We almost won. Betcha next time we'll make it."

> optimistically as in top; optimistically as in tub;
> optimistically as in mist; optimistically as in comically

"What next time?" asked Derek.

"There'll be a next time," Mike said optimistically.

Harold was glad they had entered. After all, being runner-up was pretty good even if they didn't win an award or a TV appearance.

* * *

A few days later the boys were practicing in Harold's garage. Donna came in to tell Harold he had a phone call. He ran into the house to get it.

"Harold, this is Art Wilson."

Harold couldn't believe his ears. Could it be *the* Art Wilson? All he said was, "Yes, Mr. Wilson?"

"I run the TV Dance Time Show. Maybe you've seen it. Harold, I saw the article about your band

in the paper today. I wonder if you could be ready to appear on my program tomorrow? The Four Ups had to cancel out, and we're really in a bind."

"Wow! Tomorrow! We can sure try, Mr. Wilson. I mean—we will!"

"Fine. We'll see you tomorrow at 3:30 sharp," said Mr. Wilson.

Harold said good-bye and hung up. Then he grabbed the evening paper, which was still rolled up on the coffee table. He opened the newspaper and dashed back out into the garage while trying to find the article Art Wilson had seen.

Just as he got to the garage, he spotted the article.

"Hey, you guys, look!" he yelled, waving the paper in their faces to get their attention. They all gathered around. Derek read the newspaper headline aloud:

"Southside Strummers Praised
For Performance at Festival"

The boys were all trying to read the article at once.
Mike read, "The Four Ups won first award, but this
critic says the Strummers are the most original local
youth group to appear in months. They played
Saturday afternoon for ten brief minutes in Golden
Gate Park. We hope to hear much more of them."

"Wow, we're famous!" cried Dennis. The boys were
so excited that Harold could hardly get a word in
edgewise to tell them the *big* news.

"Pipe down a sec. You haven't heard a thing yet,"
said Harold. "Art Wilson saw this article and wants
us to be on Art Wilson's TV Dance Time Show tomorrow. The Four Ups had to cancel, and we've got
the slot."

original as in upon; original as in bridge
edgewise as in hedge; edgewise as in prize;
edge + wise = edgewise

"Oh, no. The old heart just can't take it." Derek, always the clown, was slumped back on the floor, pretending to faint. The other boys started to help him up, and this ended in a tussle as usual.

At this moment Jim Sharp walked in. He leaned casually against the doorway until the scuffling had stopped. "What's all the excitement?" he asked.

Harold told him about the call from Art Wilson.

Jim didn't seem surprised. "That's what good publicity will do for you. I set up the article in today's paper for you. Just talked to the right people at the right parties—you know how it goes."

Harold didn't know "how it goes," but he didn't like to say so. He had thought that the man who wrote the article had heard them, really liked them, and written about it. I guess things aren't that simple, he thought. He didn't know why he felt so disappointed. After all, the TV appearance was the break they had been waiting for, and Jim *was* their manager.

"I told you you'd be on your way up with me as your manager," Jim bragged.

"Sure, Jim," muttered Harold, trying to sound enthusiastic.

"Come on, guys, we'd better start rehearsing if we're going on TV tomorrow," Harold told the others.

* * *

When the boys got to the television station the next day, Jim was waiting for them in the lobby. He took them upstairs to the studio, where Art Wilson came out to meet them.

Jim greeted Art Wilson like an old friend. Then he introduced him to the boys. Did Jim get us this spot with Art Wilson just as he got us the newspaper article? Harold wondered to himself. Jim was certainly acting as though he was responsible for everything that was going on.

Art was friendly to the boys.

"I've heard some great things about you," Art said. "Come on in to the studio. I'll explain how everything works in here."

He took the boys into a large room. Three cameras faced them. The boys and girls in the audience were taking their places on two sides of the room.

Art pointed to an X on the floor. "You'll be lined up behind this camera right here," he said, walking them over to one of the cameras. "When the red light goes on, you're on camera. Any questions?"

The boys shook their heads.

"Good," Art continued. "Then we're all set. Don't worry about a thing. It'll all be a snap."

Soon Art Wilson announced, "And now, presenting one of the finest local rock groups, the swinging, spectacular Southside Strummers."

Girls screamed loudly, and boys whistled. Applause filled the room. The red light on the camera lit up. The boys were on television.

After it was over, everyone ran up to them and told them what a great job they'd done. Art Wilson told them he wanted them back soon. The Strummers felt as though they were on top of the world.

"And just think of it, a month ago we couldn't get a paying job." Harold laughed.

Looking Back

Do you think Harold and the boys leave too much to chance? If you had a singing group, would you watch for opportunities to get playing dates? Why do you suppose Harold hadn't read or heard about the band contest in the park?

When the boys didn't win the contest, they were disappointed but wasted no time on self-pity. What did they do?

At the television station, Jim Sharp greeted Art Wilson as an old friend. Do you believe that they are really friends?

The Strummers were popular with the audience at the TV show. Would they have been so successful if they had not rehearsed diligently?

Do you believe steady and earnest effort should be rewarded?

Chapter 5

Looking Ahead

After the TV show, the Strummers receive more offers for playing dates than they can handle.

Jim Sharp takes credit for their public acclaim.

Even though the boys are working steadily, they have received little money for their efforts. Jim claims it is because expenses are high when a new group first begins.

Harold telephones a member of the Ultimates and learns more about Jim Sharp. You will begin to see that the Strummers could have avoided most of their problems had Harold used his good judgment months before.

In your reading, you may discover some words that are new to you. See if you can find them in the pronunciation guides.

Often when you know how to pronounce a difficult word, you will recognize it as one you use in everyday speech. If this isn't so, you should find the word in your dictionary and check it both for pronunciation and for meaning.

Some words in this chapter that you may want to look up in the dictionary are *popular*, *allowance*, *accusation*, and *outsmarted*.

High Expenses

During the weeks that followed the Art Wilson Show, the boys had more bookings than they could handle. Jim told them that he was busy making contacts for the band. He explained that if it were not for his skillful handling of their publicity, they would not be getting nearly as many jobs. Harold had to agree that ever since Jim had been their manager they had become more and more successful. However, a few fears kept gnawing at his mind. Finally, one afternoon after a jam session in his garage, he decided to discuss his doubts with the band.

"What's up, Harold? You look so serious," Mike said.

popular as in stop; popular as in young;
popular as in her

"You know," Harold said, "we've been pretty popular lately. We've had plenty of high-paying bookings. Jim's been our manager for two months now. Still we've gotten paid only a small weekly allowance."

"That's right," Mike agreed, "but he does have to pay for expenses. Remember he lent us money to pay the girls. He also spent money to advertise us."

"Don't forget our new outfits," Dennis interrupted, "and our cleaning bills. He pays for all that."

"I know he does," Harold agreed, "but still, after two months we should have more coming to us. We've been working every Friday and Saturday."

"Come to think of it, Harold, you are right," Dennis said.

"He's right, he's right, Harold is right," sang Derek, clowning around as usual.

"Cut it out," said Mike. "This is serious. What do you think we should do?" Mike asked Harold.

"Well," Harold answered slowly. "No use getting too excited yet. Why don't we go over to Jim's and talk to him about it."

"Good idea," Mike agreed. "Let's go."

The boys quickly put away their instruments and grabbed their coats. They jumped in Harold's car and started for Jim's. Jim answered the doorbell. He wore an expensive blue suit and a silk vest.

"Hi, fellows," Jim greeted the boys. "What brings you here? I was just ready to step out."

"Well," Harold began, "we've been wondering when we'll get paid some money. It's been about two months now, and all we've gotten is a small allowance."

"Glad you mentioned it," Jim replied, chewing hard on the gum in his mouth. "I've been thinking the same thing myself. I drew out some money from the band's account for each of you." Jim gave each boy ten dollars.

"Ten dollars? Is that all you're giving us after all this time?" Harold asked in amazement. "There must be more money in our account than that. Where's the bank book?"

Jim threw the book over to Harold.

"Here," Jim said. "See for yourself. After I paid all the expenses and took my own cut, that's what was left. Ten bucks for each of you."

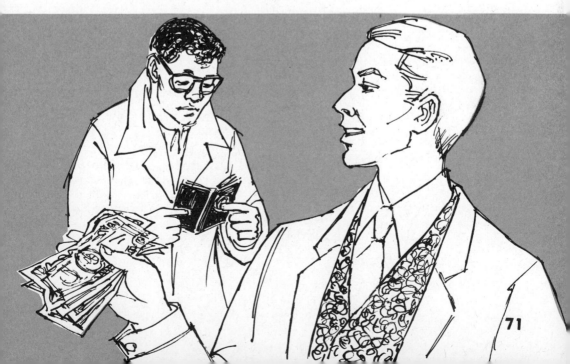

entertainment as in enter; entertainment as in pain;
entertainment as in moment

"I can't believe it! There's no money in our account," Harold said as the others crowded around to look at their account book.

"Where's a list of the expenses? We want to see it," Harold demanded.

"Sure, Harold, sure. Don't get excited. It's right here." Jim handed the list over to Harold.

Harold carefully checked the list of expenses. The others looked over his shoulder. There were charges marked for suits, cleaning, a sign, telephone bills, shirts, and more suits.

"Hey, wait a minute," Harold said. "Everything here is too high. Take this price for slacks. Our slacks didn't cost that much. I saw the bill myself."

"That's right," Jim agreed. "I bought some slacks for myself and charged them to the band."

"Who said you could do that?" Derek asked angrily.

"It's in the contract," Jim answered. He pulled out the contract and quoted, "A manager may buy suits and clothing with band funds for his own personal use. Paragraph 8."

"And what about these other items, like this one for entertainment?" Harold asked.

"Oh, that," Jim answered. "I had to throw a party to entertain the right people to get you all those newspaper clippings."

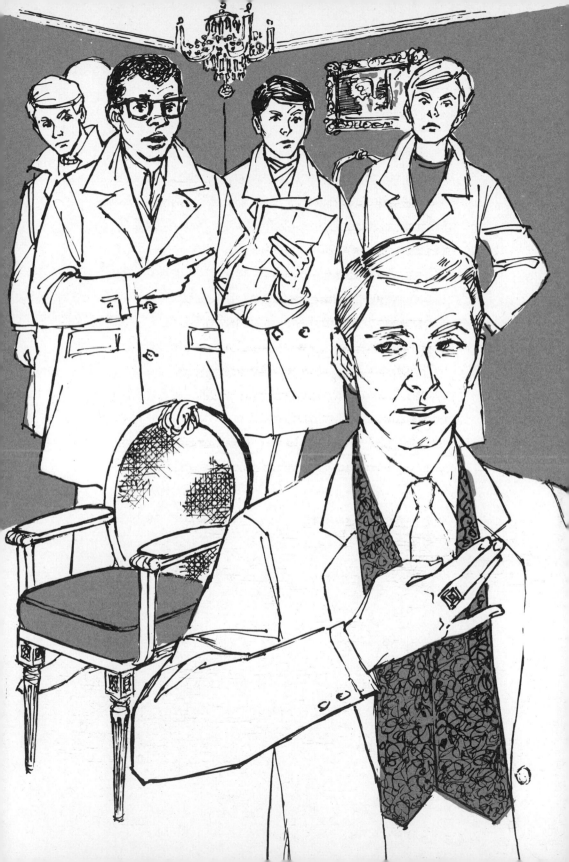

"Oh yeah?" said Harold. "If you've been making all these contacts for us, why haven't we met any of the people you've contacted? Why haven't we seen any real, solid proof that you have had anything at all to do with our success?"

Jim just shrugged, as if to say there was no point in answering such a stupid accusation.

Harold continued to look down the list of expenses. He was getting more furious every minute.

"What's this one marked dinner for two at Burson's?" Harold demanded. "I'll bet that wasn't entertaining for the band."

"Wrong," Jim replied. "A business expense according to the contract. Read paragraph 10."

Harold looked down farther on the list of expenses. He saw a charge for rent.

"Hey, wait a minute," he growled, "this is too much. What's this for Rental of Apartment at Market near Grove, the Bowman Arms? Why, we're paying the rent on this apartment!"

"Right," Jim agreed. "A business expense. This place is considered my office according to the contract. Now if you boys don't mind, I've got to be going." He pointed to the expense list in Harold's hand. "Why don't you take it home and check it against your copy of the contract? I'm sure you'll find everything in order."

"Just a minute, Jim." Harold stopped him. "Let's get one thing straight. We don't want you for a manager any more." He turned to the other boys and asked, "Do you agree?"

"We do," Derek answered, while the others nodded their heads. "We don't want anything to do with you."

"Now calm down, boys," Jim said soothingly. "This expense list is high because you're just beginning. Now you've got all kinds of jobs coming up. Even after expenses there'll be plenty of money left over for you. After all, if it wasn't for me, you'd be still playing for peanuts."

"We don't want any 'left over' money," Harold said. "You've got some nerve. We want everything but ten per cent."

"I hate to tell you this," Jim smiled, "but you've got to go through with your contract. You can't break it for another forty-six weeks. So, don't start getting any funny ideas. I'll take you to court if you break that contract. You either play for me or not at all."

"Come on, fellows. Let's get out of here," Harold said grimly, "This guy makes me sick." The boys brushed past Jim and marched out the door.

"Man, that Jim sure did take us for a ride," Dennis complained bitterly as he jumped into the car.

"We were jerks to trust him," Derek said. "That'll teach us to believe a smooth talker we don't know."

"This whole thing makes my blood boil," Harold agreed. "The worst part is that we're stuck with this contract for another forty-six weeks."

"Unless we can think of some way out of it," Derek said.

The boys drove along in silence for a while. Harold was mad at himself. Why didn't I read that contract, he asked himself. I knew the boys were depending on me. After all, they chose me as their leader. Now, if I could only think of some way out of this mess . . .

"Hey, I've got an idea," Harold cried excitedly. "Why don't we call up the Ultimates? They know Jim. Maybe they can give us some advice."

"Great idea," Dennis agreed. "Should have done it two months ago."

By now the Strummers had reached Harold's house. They dashed inside to the telephone. Harold called information for the number of the Ultimates. Then he called them.

"Hello," answered a voice on the other end of the line. "Frank here from the Ultimates. What can I do for you?"

"I'm Harold, a member of the Southside Strummers," he began. "We've been having some trouble with our manager. A fellow called Jim Sharp. He says he's managed your group."

"Did he ever!" Frank answered. "Let me tell you about that guy. He's a crook. He spent our money on high living for himself. He spent more time living it up than working for us. He didn't do us any good that I could see."

"I'm not sure he's helped us much either," Harold said. "Whenever we have a stroke of good luck he tells us he was responsible for it. But I've never really been sure if he was telling the truth."

"He knows his music," said Frank. "And he knows how to pick a group who's bound to make it. That way he doesn't have to do any work. As soon as we hired him as manager, he just relaxed and watched the money pour in. Until we broke the contract."

"How did you break the contract?" Harold asked excitedly.

"Simple," Frank replied. "We were under eighteen. We found out the contract wasn't legal in this state because our parents didn't sign with us."

"Thanks a lot, Frank," said Harold with relief.

"By the way, Harold, do you know where we can get hold of that crook?" asked Frank. "He still owes us a pile of money."

"He'll probably be at our performance Saturday night at the Biltmore Auditorium," replied Harold.

"Well, if he is, get ready for some action," said Frank.

"What do you mean?" asked Harold. "What are you going to do?"

"I don't know, exactly. But a lot of scores are going to be settled. I'll see you there, Harold."

"Okay, Frank, see you," said Harold, hanging up.

"We *can* break our contract, guys. We're under age, and the contract isn't legal. Wait until Old Sharpie hears this."

"Ha, Ha," Mike yelled. "He outsmarted himself by getting us to sign so quick."

"Whoopee, whoopee, I see, I see, Jim ain't going to live for free, on me, on us, on me," Derek sang. He had grabbed his guitar, strumming it softly, and clowning around as only Derek could.

"I can hardly wait to tell him," Dennis said.

"Yeah," Harold agreed, "let's give him the bad news just before we go on at the Biltmore."

Looking Back

Harold had distrusted Jim Sharp almost from the beginning. Do you think he should have discussed his suspicions with the group long before he did? Would this have helped to avoid their problems? Remember how the boys were in the beginning of the story. Could Harold have convinced them that Jim was not a good man to be their manager?

Were you surprised to find that Jim was taking unfair advantage of the Strummers by using their success only for his own profit?

Did you know that a young person who is legally a minor cannot enter into most contracts? For a contract with a minor to be valid, it must also be signed by those legally responsible for his welfare. In your state, how old does a person have to be to enter into contracts?

Chapter 6

Looking Ahead

The Strummers arrive early for their playing date at the Biltmore Auditorium. A crowd is waiting outside the auditorium to hear the Strummers. The Strummers feel that they are on top.

When Jim arrives, Harold tells him that the Strummers no longer want him as their manager. Jim is ready for an argument, but he is stopped by the "action" that Frank of the Ultimates had promised.

The crowd is let into the auditorium, and the Strummers know that they are really on their way.

Remember, it is good practice to look in a dictionary for any words that you do not understand in your reading. Some words that you may want to look up are *chorused*, *paled*, *downright*, and *miserable*.

On Top

The Southside Strummers arrived early the night of their big Biltmore performance. Harold felt anxious. He wondered what "action" Frank had in mind for Jim Sharp.

"Wow, get a look at all those kids waiting to get in," Mike said as they walked past the box office.

"Yeah, when you play at the Biltmore, you've reached the top of the heap in this town." Derek grinned.

Once inside, the boys quickly set up their equipment and tuned their instruments.

equipment as in it; equipment as in quick;
equipment as in moment

"Say, Harold, did you square it away with the Biltmore manager on how the check is to be made out?" Derek asked.

"You bet," Harold replied. "From now on, we play the performance, we get the pay. I wish Jim would show up. I'm getting itchy to tell him where to get off."

"Me, too," the other Strummers chorused. Finally they saw Jim coming through a side door.

"Hi, guys," Jim said in a friendly voice. "You're on top now. Didn't I tell you I could do it for you? Hope you've gotten over your silly idea about walking out on our contract."

"We don't think it's such a silly idea," Harold said. "You can take that contract and yourself right out of our lives. We can't afford you any more."

"Now just a minute! I told you the contract was good for another forty-six weeks. There's nothing you can do about that. Let's not have any unfriendly scenes," Jim said angrily.

"We're not unfriendly. We just don't like to be taken for a ride—especially since we're under age.

Or hadn't you thought about that when you were so anxious for us to sign. Your contract isn't worth the paper it's written on. So shove off," Harold said.

Jim opened his mouth to argue, when two police officers and a young man came through the stage door. They walked straight up to Jim. Jim paled when he saw the young man.

"That's him, officer." The young man pointed at Jim. The policemen walked over and handcuffed Jim.

"Now, wait a minute. There must be some misunderstanding, Frank," Jim whined.

---

paled as in page; paled as in sailed

> downright as in town; downright as in fight;
>   down + right = downright
> miserable as in his; miserable as in her;
>   miserable as in useable

"There's no misunderstanding," Frank said. "The Ultimates have been looking for you for a long time. Not only did you spend our money on high expenses, but you took our last check and left town—or so we thought until Harold called us. We had broken the contract before that performance, so you can't claim expenses. It was just downright stealing."

"I can explain, I can explain," Jim whined.

"Do your explaining to the judge," one of the officers said, leading Jim out the door.

After they left, Harold introduced the other boys to Frank.

"We sure thank you for helping us find a way to break that miserable contract," Harold said.

"We should be the ones to thank you," Frank replied. "If it hadn't been for your call, Jim might have gone on taking other groups for a ride. Now he'll pay for his mischief."

Just then the auditorium door opened, and a crowd of teenagers rushed in. They began screaming for the group to start playing.

"I'd say good luck, but it looks like you already have all the luck you need," Frank called as he walked out the door.

The Southside Strummers started playing their

first number, and the crowd went wild. Girls screamed, and boys stomped and whistled. The Strummers spotted their parents, seated in the first row.

Derek started his solo. "We're on our way . . ."

Looking Back

Now that you have finished the book, consider how the boys managed to accomplish the goal they set for themselves.

Mr. Brown helped them twice. How did he do this? Donna and Janet helped by making shirts for the Strummers. Who else helped them?

Consider how things might have been if these persons had not believed that the Strummers were a talented group. If the Strummers had not been earnest and hard-working, do you think that these persons would have helped them?

Do you believe that Jim Sharp deserved to be arrested? Have you ever known anyone who habitually profited unfairly from the hard work and talents of others? Such persons are sometimes called "parasites." Was Jim a parasite?

What qualities did the Strummers have that would make you believe that they deserved to succeed?

Vocabularies

Your teacher may ask you to prepare one or more assignments using the following vocabularies:

V-1	V-2	V-3
accusation	admirers	advance
audience	auditorium	bandstand
costumes	critics	decision
entertainment	enthusiastically	equipment
festival	gratitude	guarantee
instrument	intermission	interrupted
material	microphone	miniature
outsmarted	percentage	persuade
reception	rehearsal	reputation
scholarship	skeptical	soloist

V-4	V-5	V-6
allowance	approached	approaching
baritone	chorused	contract
downright	edgewise	embarrassed
experience	fabric	fantastically
guitar	hesitantly	improvised
introduced	issue	legal
miserable	optimistically	original
popular	possibilities	publicity
rhythmic	sandwiched	saxophone
spectacular	sponsoring	vocalist

ACKNOWLEDGMENTS

We wish to express gratitude to the people who have lent invaluable assistance in the preparation of this book, and to thank in particular:

Randi Slaughter

Photo Credits

Susan Elting (Courtesy Fillmore Auditorium), cover, pages 25, 26, 27, 28, 37, 38, 55, 56